SHERLOCK HOLMES'

Puzzles of Deduction

Tom Bullimore
Illustrated by Ian Anderson

Sterling Publishing
New York

Library of Congress Cataloging-in-Publication Data

Bullimore, Tom.
    Sherlock Holmes' puzzles of deduction / by Tom Bullimore :
illustrated by Ian Anderson.
        p.   cm.
    Includes index.
    ISBN 0-8069-9675-7
    1. Puzzles. 2. Detective and mystery stories. 3. Doyle, Arthur
Conan, Sir, 1859–1930—Characters—Sherlock Holmes. I. Title.
GV1507.D4B86 1997
793.73—dc21   96-49893
                                                            CIP

    3   5   7   9   10   8   6   4   2

Published by Sterling Publishing Company, Inc.
387 Park Avenue South, New York, N.Y. 10016
© 1997 by Tom Bullimore
Distributed in Canada by Sterling Publishing
% Canadian Manda Group, One Atlantic Avenue, Suite 105
Toronto, Ontario, Canada M6K 3E7
Distributed in Great Britain and Europe by Cassell PLC
Wellington House, 125 Strand, London WC2R 0BB, England
Distributed in Australia by Capricorn Link (Australia) Pty Ltd.
P.O. Box 6651, Baulkham Hills, Business Centre, NSW 2153, Australia
Manufactured in the United States of America
All rights reserved

Sterling ISBN 0-8069-9675-7

Contents

"Take a look at this, Watson," said Holmes as he passed a coded message to his colleague.

The message read:

> TO SHERLOCK HOLMES,
> T5M5RR5W4W4LLST32LTH3CR5WN
> J3W3LSTH4SW4LLB3MYGR32T3STTR46MPH.
>   MORIARTY.

"What does it all mean, Holmes?" exclaimed Watson.

"To find that out, Watson, we must break the code. The numbers obviously represent letters."

"But he doesn't use the numbers one or zero, Holmes," said Watson.

"That is simply because they could be mistaken for the letters I and O, Watson," said Holmes as he set about breaking the code.

Can you decipher the message?

Sherlock Holmes and Dr. Watson had apprehended three men suspected of carrying out the Clapham bank robbery. The three men, Fish, Giles and Hill, were taken to Scotland Yard, where they were interviewed by Inspector Lestrade. As Lestrade noted down the age of each of the men, he was aware that if he reversed each of the digits of their age, all three men would still remain the same age. Lestrade also noticed that Fish was only a third the age of Giles, who in turn was twice the age of Hill. The combined age of all three men was 121 yrs.

How old was each of the three men?

While wearing one of his famous disguises, Sherlock Holmes followed a suspect through London's busy streets. The suspect entered two shops. In order not to look suspicious, Holmes purchased an item in each of the shops. In the first shop Holmes spent one-fourth of all his money, and in the second shop he spent one-fourth of what remained.

If Holmes spent £21 in total, how much did he have to begin with?

Sherlock Holmes and Dr. Watson had been spectators at the annual Scotland Yard athletics meeting. Inspector Lestrade had done extremely well for his team. He was first in two events and second in another. Lestrade's team had scored a total of 25 points, making them outright winners of the whole meeting. In each event points were awarded for first, second and third place. Lestrade's team had gained their points by winning four events, coming in second in two and taking a third place in another.

How many points did Inspector Lestrade score for his team?

Aston Avenue was a private row of only five houses numbered 1, 2, 3, 4 and 5. The owners of these houses were Messrs. Jones, White, Smith, Green and Brown. All five houses had recently been robbed and Sherlock Holmes called to speak with each of the owners. Unfortunately, all five were not at home. Holmes spoke with a passerby and was able to record the following facts:

1. Jones lived two doors to the left of Smith.
2. Brown had Green living on his right.
3. Both White and Brown lived in an even-numbered house.

From the above can you determine which house on Aston Avenue Mr. Green lived in?

Sherlock Holmes had received two telegrams from the infamous Professor Moriarty within a space of 3 hours. The first was a threat against the famous detective's life, while the second said that he, the professor, had organized a present for Holmes. The remainder of the second telegram contained the following riddle:

> He who makes it, makes it to sell,
> He who buys it, does not use it,
> He who uses it, does not know it.

Watson read both telegrams. "It doesn't make sense to me, Holmes," said Watson. "First he threatens your life and then he organizes a present for you."

"Solve the riddle, Watson. Then you'll see that it makes sense," replied Holmes.

What was it that Moriarty intended to send Holmes?

Sherlock Holmes was questioning three men who had been witness to a murder, Messrs. Franks, Richards and Andrews. By coincidence, their first names were Richard, Frank and Andrew. Holmes remarked to Mr. Richards on this.

"Yes, I noticed that as well," he replied. "But none of us have the first name that matches our surname. My first name happens to be Andrew."

Can you give the full name of all three witnesses?

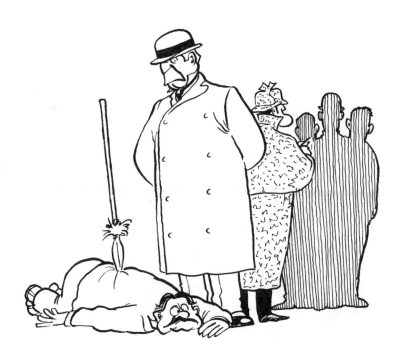

Sherlock Holmes sat by the fire at 221b Baker Street, studying some information on a note.

"What's that you're reading, Holmes?" asked Watson as he entered.

"It's a list of houses on Fitzroy Street that have all been robbed in the last 6 days by Professor Moriarty."

Watson glanced at the list, which read:

> Mon   No. 4
> Tues No. 16
> Wed   No. 12
> Thur No. 3
> Fri   No. 7
> Sat   No. 28

"Great Scott!" exclaimed Watson. "And today's Sunday. He'll probably strike again tonight."

"He will, Watson," replied Holmes. "But this time we'll be waiting inside the house for him."

Which house on Fitzroy Street will Moriarty rob next?

Sherlock Holmes, Dr. Watson and Inspector Lestrade were enjoying a cup of tea in the study of 221b Baker Street, when they were called away on an urgent matter. Each grabbed an overcoat and rushed from the house. It turned out that all three had grabbed the wrong overcoat.

"This coat is much too tight on me," remarked Lestrade to the person wearing Watson's coat.

Whose overcoat was each of them wearing?

Dr. Watson was sitting in the study of 221b Baker Street, passing the time working on a word puzzle. Five of the words were causing him problems.

      1. EALINE
      2. CTHEDRL
      3. FORBAR
      4. HOGOLIN
      5. SIENE

Each of the words has two letters missing. For each word it is the same letter that needs to be inserted twice. The missing letters are A, B, C, D and E, but not necessarily in this order.

Can you help Dr. Watson out?

Dr. Watson was taking a stroll through Hyde Park with his sister. As they walked, Watson pointed to a boy sitting on a bench. "That boy is my nephew," stated Watson.

"Well, he's not my nephew," replied the woman.

Can you explain this?

"I'm stuck on the crossword, Holmes," said Watson. "It's an eight-letter word containing four G's."

Holmes glanced at the crossword and laughed.

"It's no laughing matter!" exclaimed Watson.

"Oh, but it is, my dear Watson, it is," said Holmes.

Can you deduce the common English word that Watson is looking for?

Sherlock Holmes arrested the butler of the Westwood mansion for poisoning the entire Westwood family. After confessing, the butler went on to explain to Holmes just exactly how it was done. He filled a wineglass half full of wine, and another glass twice the size one-third full of wine. He then topped up each glass with poison before pouring the contents of both glasses into an empty wine decanter.

Can you deduce how much of the mixture is wine and how much is poison?

To pass the time while traveling on a long train journey, Sherlock Holmes set his colleague, Dr. Watson, a little teaser to work out. See the diagram below:

7			=19
		5	=16
	3		=10

‖	‖	‖	＼
15	16	14	17

"What do you want me to do with this, Holmes?" asked Watson.

"Simple, my dear Watson. Insert the following numbers in their proper place so that each column adds up to the number indicated. The missing numbers are: 4, 6, 1, 2, 8, 9."

By the time their train journey had ended, Watson had failed to complete the teaser correctly.

Can you do better?

"I've counted up my bank balance in 30 seconds flat, Holmes," said Watson. "If I hadn't become a doctor I think I would have been a mathematician."

"Is that so, Watson? Then perhaps you can do this simple addition for me. Using the same three digits, write out the addition that totals 24."

"Great Scott, Holmes. That's simple," cried Watson

"Ah, Watson, there is one piece of information I must add. You cannot use the number 8."

"Oh," said Watson, "That changes things slightly."

Can you work it out?

Sherlock Holmes scribbled something on a piece of paper and passed it to Dr. Watson. "Can you identify the next letter in the sequence?" asked Holmes.

The sequence read: T T T F F S S E ?

Watson had several guesses before he got it right.

How quickly can you find the answer?

Sherlock Holmes and Dr. Watson were sitting by the fire in the study of 221b Baker Street. They sat in silence for a long time, before Holmes spoke. "Tell me, Watson. What is it that occurs four times in every week, twice in every month, but only once in a year?"

"I've no idea, Holmes," grunted Watson.

Can you supply the answer?

Sherlock Holmes and Dr. Watson were running after a criminal in a crowded London street. They turned a corner only to find that the criminal was nowhere to be seen. Holmes turned to a beggar sitting at the side of the road. "Did you happen to see a man wearing a tall black hat and a cape pass this way?"

"Yes," replied the beggar.

"Which direction did he take?" asked Watson.

"Well, when I first saw him he was facing due east, but then he did a right turn, followed by an about turn, before taking a left turn and heading off in that direction."

Which way did the criminal go?

Sherlock Holmes called at the house of Lord Winton on a matter of business. While he sat in the study waiting for his lordship to appear, he found himself surrounded by the children of the house. Lord Winton had nine children in all. The children had been born at regular intervals—18 months between each birth. Holmes discovered that John, the oldest child, is five times the age of Robert, the youngest child.

How old is Robert?

A murderer had weighted down the body of his victim and dumped him in the Thames. Unknown to the murderer, the point where he dumped the body was much shallower than he had thought. Sherlock Holmes was called to the scene, where he discovered that the body was standing upright in the water. One-fourth of the victim was buried in the mud, five-eighths of the body was covered by water and the remaining $9\frac{1}{2}$ inches protruded from the water.

Can you determine the height of the victim in feet and inches?

Sherlock Holmes, Dr. Watson and Inspector Lestrade were all involved in the solving of a recent murder. The day after the case was concluded, all three wrote individual reports on the crime. The combined number of pages written was ninety-nine. Lestrade wrote five more pages than Holmes, who in turn had submitted seventeen more pages than Watson.

How many pages did each of them write?

Sherlock Holmes, Dr. Watson, Mrs. Hudson, Sgt. Black and Inspector Lestrade were all in court as witnesses for the prosecution against Professor Moriarty. Sherlock Holmes was called before Watson, but after Mrs. Hudson. Sgt. Black was called before Lestrade, but after Watson.

Can you identify the order in which the witnesses were called?

Professor Moriarty had trapped Holmes and Watson in a room with no windows and only one door. After a few minutes, they could hear the sound of a pump starting up and within moments the room began to fill with water. "Great Scott, we're going to drown!" shouted Watson.

Holmes moved over to the door, where he found it to be secured by a combination lock. There was a note pinned to the door in Moriarty's handwriting. The note revealed that the combination to the lock contained six numbers. The sum of the first two numbers was 69. The next two totalled 79. And the last two 29. At this point Holmes remembered something that Moriarty had said as he had closed them in the room. "It will help you, Holmes, if you remember that the difference between the first and second, the third and fourth, and the fifth and sixth is 13 in each case!" Holmes smiled as he set to work on the combination lock.

Can you find the six numbers that would open the door and release Holmes and Watson?

While serving a ten-year prison sentence inside London's Wormwood Scrubs prison, Professor Moriarty hatched a plan to make his escape. From beneath his cell he would tunnel the 30 feet across the courtyard, continue tunnelling under the 3-feet-thick wall and emerge, in some wasteland, some 10 feet from the wall. Spurred on by the thought of freedom, Moriarty found that he was able to double his efforts each day.

If it took him 28 days to cover the complete distance to reach the exact point of his planned escape, how long did it take him to reach halfway?

Sherlock Holmes, Dr. Watson and Inspector Lestrade shared a cab to Euston Station, where they would each catch a train to separate destinations.

1. Holmes would not be taking the train to Brighton.
2. Watson wasn't taking the train to Manchester.
3. Lestrade wasn't taking the Edinburgh train.
4. The Brighton train left before Watson's train.

From the above information, can you discover the intended destinations of all three?

Sherlock Holmes received an urgent telegram from a client. The client felt certain that his life was in danger. Holmes and Watson hurried to his lodgings only to find that they were too late. The man had been murdered minutes before they had arrived.

"I found him lying there," said the landlady. "Before he died he muttered something about belonging to a secret club and quoted the number 92."

"Damned strange thing to say, Holmes," said Watson.

Holmes nodded in agreement. "Did he say anything else?" Holmes asked the landlady.

"I asked him who had done this terrible thing to him, but he just repeated the number 92!" she answered.

Holmes thanked her for her help and discharged her. He then proceeded to search the dead man's room. He came across a letter addressed to the man that was from the other three members of the secret club. Their names were Mr. Wilson, Mr. Updike and Mr. Brown. In the top left of the letter was the name of the dead man, Mr. Smith (Code 69). From this, Holmes deduced that he had been murdered by another member of the club, and that the number that he had uttered to the landlady was in fact the code number of the murderer.

Holmes was then quickly able to supply the name of the killer. Can you?

Holmes glanced at a note that had been slipped under the door of 221b Baker Street.

"What is it, Holmes?" asked Watson, seeing the concern on the face of his colleague.

"It's a note from Moriarty. He intends to kidnap a prominent member of Parliament, and he has sent us a riddle as to the identity of the victim."

The riddle read: GREAT WISE OLD MAN, AT WILL.

Whom did Moriarty intend to kidnap?

While solving a recent fraud case, Sherlock Holmes interviewed a man, his three sons and each of the son's three sons.

From the above information can you answer the following:
1. How many pairs of brothers did Holmes interview?
2. How many pairs of uncles and nephews did he interview?

Sherlock Holmes sat with three gentlemen in a railway carriage as he travelled to Brighton. From their conversation, Holmes noted the following snippets of information: Arthur is older than the man with brown hair, but younger than the accountant. Bert is younger than the man with grey hair, while Clive is older than the bald-headed man. The banker is the doctor's younger brother.

Can you give the occupation of each of the men and the color of their hair (if they have any)?

Moriarty and his two partners in crime, Fingers and Porky, sat looking at the diamonds piled on the table in front of them. There was a knock at the door, which Porky answered. Mr. X, the brains behind the diamond robbery, entered. Moriarty sent Porky to check the surrounding area to make sure that Mr. X had not been followed. Mr. X then took Porky's seat at the table. They sat in silence for several moments, until Moriarty bent forward and took half of the diamonds plus one from the pile. Mr. X then took two-thirds of what remained, placed them in his pocket and, without a word, left the building. Fingers then took two-thirds of what remained and placed them in a bag. He smiled at Moriarty and took one more diamond, which he quickly shoved into the top pocket of his coat.

When Porky returned, he glanced down at the solitary diamond lying on the table. "Is this all I get, one measly diamond?" he grunted.

How many diamonds had originally been on the table?

"What are you up to now, Watson?" asked Holmes as he entered the study.

Watson stopped pounding away at his typewriter and glanced up at Holmes.

"I'm writing a mystery novel," announced Watson. "This is one of the many puzzles in the mystery. Can you tell me the next letter in this sequence of letters?"

The sequence read: Z X C V B N ?

Can you identify the next letter in the sequence?

Professor Moriarty had tunnelled into the vault of a well-known London bank. When he was absolutely certain that his activities had not triggered off an alarm, he proceeded to break open a number of safe-deposit boxes.

If Moriarty had robbed the safe-deposit boxes in the following order, can you identify the number of the next box he would force open?

Safe-deposit boxes robbed: Numbers 59, 49, 58, 50, 57, 51, 56, ?

Lord Knight invited Sherlock Holmes, Dr. Watson and Inspector Lestrade to spend the weekend at his country estate. After showing the excellent stable facilities, Lord Knight suggested that they, along with the stables' head boy, Martin, should all take part in a horse race around the boundaries of the estate. Everybody readily agreed.

The last horse to finish was Fair Sensation. Ivory Tower finished first. Watson rode Kestrel. Lestrade's horse finished fourth. Holmes didn't finish second. Lord Knight finished three places behind Spring Goddess.

From the above information can you identify:
a) who rode Tinkerbell?
b) which horse Martin rode?

Holmes and Watson passed beneath a clock tower as they returned from the theatre. At that very moment, the clock struck midnight.

"Great Scott," cried Watson as he covered his ears with his hands. "That's loud enough to make one deaf!"

Holmes smiled. "Ah, just think, Watson," he said. "If that clock was turned into a 24-hour clock, it would strike twenty-four times at midnight."

Watson was far from amused at the prospect.

If the clock had indeed been turned into a 24-hour clock, can you figure out how many times it would strike in twenty-four hours?

Sherlock Holmes and Dr. Watson took a break from crime solving by spending a relaxing day fishing on the Thames. They had spent the better part of the morning without as much as a bite when all of a sudden Watson's rod almost broke in two. "Great Scott, Holmes," he shouted. "I've got a whopper on the line!" It took Watson all of 50 minutes to reel the fish in. It was indeed a whopper. The tail weighed 9 pounds. The head weighed as much as the tail and one-third of the body combined, and the body weighed as much as the head and tail combined.

What was the weight of the whole fish?

Sherlock Holmes, Dr. Watson and Mrs. Hudson left Baker Street to spend an evening at the theatre. In the foyer, they met Inspector Lestrade and Sgt. Baxter. All five had a drink in the theatre bar before taking their seats to enjoy the performance. All five sat in the same row together, taking up the seats numbered 35, 36, 37, 38 and 39.

From the information below can you identify the seats occupied by Inspector Lestrade and Sergeant Baxter?

1. Watson sat to the left of Holmes, but not directly.
2. Sgt. Baxter sat in an odd-numbered seat with Holmes directly on his right.
3. Mrs. Hudson sat to the left of Lestrade, but not directly.

Sherlock Holmes apprehended three muggers in a back alley just off Fenchurch Street. They were found to be in possession of £227 between them. Albert had £35 more than Bobby, while Craig had £7 more than Albert.

How much did each of them have?

Dr. Watson, who had been keeping an eye on events at Lady McBride's dinner party, reported back to Sherlock Holmes at 221b Baker Street.

"I need to know the arrival times of the guests, Watson," said Holmes.

Watson glanced at his note pad. "Yes, here it is. The arrival times are as follows," said Watson. "7:30, 7:45, 7:50, 7:59, 8:05, with the last guest arriving at 8:20."

"Very good, Watson," said Holmes. "But I need to know just exactly which guest arrived at which time."

"Oh," said Watson, somewhat embarrassed. "I didn't write that down, Holmes."

Eventually Watson was able to pass the following information to Holmes:

1. Lady Barclay, who wasn't the first to arrive, arrived before Lord Hadden.
2. Sir Harry Trump arrived 15 minutes after Lord Winterbottom.
3. It was one of the ladies who arrived 6 minutes after Sir John Penn.
4. Lady James arrived 15 minutes before Lord Hadden.

Can you deduce the exact arrival time of each of the six guests?

Holmes, Watson and Inspector Lestrade were searching for a criminal by the name of Black-Eyed Jack. When he wasn't committing crimes, Jack was known to be a frequent visitor to many taverns in London. The three of them split up and between them they called on fifty-seven taverns before Black-Eyed Jack was found and arrested.

If Lestrade visited three more taverns than Watson, who in turn visited three more taverns than Holmes, how many taverns did each of them visit?

Sherlock Holmes was travelling by train from London to Brighton. Five other gentlemen shared the compartment with him. They were Messrs. Andrews, Baker, Clark, Dawson and Easton. It turned out that each of these gentlemen lived on a London street that bore the name of one of the others.

From the following information can you match up each of the five men with the street where he lived?

1. Mr. Andrews sat between Sherlock Holmes and the other gentleman who lived on Baker Street.
2. Mr. Baker, who sat opposite Mr. Dawson, had the gentleman who lived on Clark Street sitting next to him.
3. The gentleman opposite Holmes lived on Easton Street.

To pass the time on a long train journey from London to Dartmoor, Sherlock Holmes, Dr. Watson and Inspector Lestrade held a general knowledge quiz. Each player was awarded a point for a correct answer. By the time they had reached their destination a total of eighty-four points had been scored. Watson had finished the game with twice as many points as Lestrade. If Lestrade's total was multiplied by three, it equalled the number of points obtained by Holmes.

How many points did each of them score?

Professor Moriarty was selling stolen goods at an East End marketplace. The goods were all marked at the retail price of either £5 or £2. In order to sell as much as he could in the shortest possible time, Moriarty decided to offer the goods at half their marked price. During the course of the day Moriarty sold exactly forty-five items and collected a total of £90.

How many of the cheaper-priced items did Moriarty sell?

Sherlock Holmes was sitting by the fire at 221b Baker Street when this coded message arrived from Inspector Lestrade.

3 15 13 5   17 21 9 3 11 12 25,   8 15 12 13 5 19.
20 8 5 18 5 19   19 20 18 1 14 7 5   7 15 9 14 7 19   15 14
1 20   2 1 19 11 5 18 22 9 12 12 5   8 1 12 12.

Can you decipher the message?

Miss Aldridge, who ran a large boarding house in Acton town, had sent a telegram to Sherlock Holmes requesting his help on a matter of great importance. Within an hour of receiving the telegram, Holmes and his assistant, Dr. Watson, arrived at the large house on Acton High Street.

"I'm quite concerned," said Miss Aldridge as she led them into the parlor. "I'm positive that one of my guests is trying to poison me."

"How many guests do you have?" asked Watson as he sat down in front of the roaring fire.

"Quite a few," replied the old lady. "Half of them are salesmen, a quarter of them teach at the local college and one-seventh are shop owners. There are also three widowed ladies, but I don't suspect any of them."

From the above information, can you figure out how many guests lived at the boarding house?

Inspector Lestrade called at 221b Baker Street to discuss a case with Sherlock Holmes. As they talked, Mrs. Hudson brought a pot of tea and a tray of freshly baked cakes. Lestrade, who was feeling quite hungry, demolished 1/3 of the cakes as he listened to Holmes's views on the case. When Holmes had finished talking, he proceeded to eat 1/3 of what remained. Doctor Watson joined them in the study a half hour later when he returned from visiting a patient. He also took a fancy to the cakes and ate 1/3 of what remained. A short time later, Mrs. Hudson cleared the table and found that there were 8 cakes left.

How many cakes had originally been on the tray?

Sherlock Holmes arrested 40-year-old Harry Barns and his 13-year-old assistant Jack as they made their getaway from a large house in Knightsbridge. It annoyed Holmes that Harry should use someone so young to help in his criminal activities.

"I need him to squeeze through partly opened windows, Mr. Holmes," said Harry. "I've been using him since I was four times his age."

How many years ago was Harry four times the age of Jack?

Sherlock Holmes and Dr. Watson were tracking an escaped convict across the Yorkshire Dales without the use of a map or compass. Neither of them had been to Yorkshire before. They came to a crossroads where the signpost had been knocked down. They wanted to go to a village called Littlethorpe, which was one of the four villages on the signpost.

How could they be sure of going in the right direction without asking anybody?

"I'm puzzled," said Lady Ashton to Sherlock Holmes. "One of my four servants has stolen my gold bracelet. I've questioned each of them, but I'm still none the wiser. Branson, the butler, said that Smythe, the gardener, did it, while Mary, the maid, said Smythe had told her that Branson did it. Smythe told me Branson did it, and Wilson, the handyman, said he knew which one was the thief but he did not wish to say." Lady Ashton sighed, then continued, "I've known Branson and Smythe for many years and I've never known either of them to tell the truth."

Sherlock Holmes smiled as he filled his pipe. "Assuming that the butler and the gardener have not changed their ways, and that Mary and Wilson are telling the truth, it is quite a simple task to deduce which one of them is the thief," said Holmes.

Can you work out which one of the staff stole the bracelet?

Sherlock Holmes interviewed five witnesses to a murder: a man and his wife and their three children, David, Brenda and Thomas. As Holmes jotted down some of the personal details of the family, he noticed that the difference between the parents' ages was the same as between David and Brenda, and between Brenda and Thomas. The ages of Brenda and David multiplied together equalled the age of their father, while the ages of Brenda and Thomas multiplied together equalled the age of their mother. The combined ages of all the family members was ninety years.

Can you deduce the age of each person?

Following the hideous death of Sir John Updike, Sherlock Holmes apprehended two likely suspects. They were simply known as Frank and Fred. Holmes knew little of the two men except that Fred could never tell the truth and Frank could never lie. One of the men made the following statement to Holmes: "The other one said he is Fred."

Can you deduce which of the two men made the statement?

Sherlock Holmes handed a piece of notepaper to Dr. Watson. The following sequence of letters was written on the paper:

O T T F F S R S E N T.

"One of those letters does not belong to the series, Watson," said Holmes.

Can you identify the letter that doesn't belong?

Professor Moriarty was sitting in his prison cell, where he would spend the next few days before his court appearance on a robbery charge. In order to pass some time he dealt six playing cards face down in a row on the cell table. He then gave his cellmate the following information:

1. The King of Spades had the Ace of Hearts and the Ace of Diamonds to its left.
2. The Queen of Diamonds had the Ten of Clubs to its right.
3. The Queen of Hearts is separated from the spade by two cards.
4. Three cards separate the two hearts.

Can you identify the positions of all six cards?

Sherlock Holmes, Dr. Watson, Mrs. Hudson and Inspector Lestrade all took part in a pie-eating competition. Between them they ate fifty-eight pies. Holmes ate half as many pies as Watson, who in turn ate 2/3 of the amount eaten by Mrs. Hudson. Lestrade ate 1/4 of the combined number of pies eaten by Mrs. Hudson and Dr. Watson.

How many pies did each of them eat?

Dr. Watson glanced up from his crossword puzzle. "Can you think of a common English word with three consecutive double letters?" he asked Sherlock Holmes, who sat opposite.

"I think you should consult your accountant on that one, Watson," Holmes replied with a smile.

Can you find the word Watson is looking for?

Sherlock Holmes and Dr. Watson were enjoying a quiet drink in the members' lounge of the Criminologist's Club when four men entered by way of the private office. "Ah, here come the four new committee members," announced Holmes.

"I don't recognize any of them," said Watson.

"Before you stand the chairman, vice-chairman, treasurer and secretary," replied Holmes. "Their surnames are Hopkins, Smythe, White and Knight."

Holmes then went on to explain that the treasurer and the chairman were cousins, that Hopkins and Smythe were not related to each other, that the vice-chairman's wife was a well-known actress, and that the secretary was engaged to Lord Winterbottom's daughter.

He also pointed out that White and the treasurer were not on speaking terms, and that Hopkins and White were the only ones who were married.

Can you identify each committee member's new position within the club?

"I'm bored," said Dr. Watson to Sherlock Holmes. "This train journey seems to be going on forever."

Sherlock Holmes smiled at his companion and took a sheet of paper from his coat pocket. On the sheet of paper Holmes drew a large square. He then divided this square into sixteen squares (see diagram). He then took four coins from his pocket and asked Watson to place each coin on one of the squares in such a way that no two coins ended up in the same row either horizontally, vertically or diagonally.

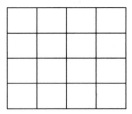

Can you achieve this? (There are several possible solutions.)

A special meeting was held at the Criminologist's Club to elect a new chairman. Sir John Blackstock received 10% of all the votes cast. Lord Halifax received 30%. Walter Winston received eighteen votes in all, while Sherlock Holmes collected the remaining thirty-six votes. Five of the members present at the meeting elected to abstain from voting.

How many members attended the meeting?

Sherlock Holmes and Dr. Watson had spent several hours observing a band of pickpockets stealing pocket watches in a crowded marketplace.

"I've noticed that two pickpockets can pick two pockets in two seconds," said Watson, somewhat proud of his observation.

"That being the case," replied Holmes, "how many pockets can six pickpockets pick in six seconds?"

Can you work it out?

After dinner one evening, Mrs. Hudson opened a box of chocolates. The box contained forty-five sweets. There were twice as many soft centers as there were hard centers. She offered Dr. Watson first choice from the box.

What were the odds that Watson would select a chocolate with a hard center?

"It was undoubtedly one of the staff who murdered Lord Back-water," said Sherlock Holmes to Dr. Watson. "Have you interviewed them?"

"Yes," replied Watson, glancing at his notes. "It turns out that the maid is the sister of the butler's granddaughter, who, in turn, is the gardener's brother's mother."

From the above information, can you tell how the gardener and the butler were related?

After some clever groundwork by Sherlock Holmes, Inspector Lestrade was able to arrest three criminals. Between them they were charged with thirty-seven different offenses.

If Harold was charged with five more offenses than John, and Robert was charged with six more offenses than Harold, how many offenses had each of them committed?

Sherlock Holmes called at the home of one of the Baker Street residents in order to reward him for his help in solving a recent crime. Holmes had always thought that the young boy was an only child. How surprised he was to discover that this was not the case. The young boy had quite a number of brothers and sisters. Each boy had two-thirds the number of brothers as he had sisters, while each girl had an equal number of brothers and sisters.

Can you tell exactly how many boys and girls were in the family?

Sherlock Holmes and Dr. Watson apprehended five pickpockets during a charity cricket match. The five were well known to the duo by their nicknames: Fingers, Swifty, Lefty, Speedy and Shifty. Between them they had gathered £150 before they were caught. Fingers had more money than Swifty, but less than Lefty. Speedy had more money than Shifty, but less than Swifty.

From the above information, can you identify which pickpocket had the most money and which one had the least?

After a recent robbery, Professor Moriarty found himself with three piles of coins on the table in front of him. In all, there were 2,350 coins. Pile one had 500 more coins than pile two, while pile two had 400 more coins than pile three.

How many coins were in each of the three piles?

On a cold winter's evening Sherlock Holmes and Dr. Watson sat in the comfort of a blazing fire at their residence at 221b Baker Street. After a long bout of silence Sherlock Holmes spoke. "Take the word 'sparkling,' Watson. Take away one letter so as to leave a new word. Then continue this procedure, leaving a new word on each occasion until you are left with a one-letter word."

Watson sat for some time before finally coming up with an answer.

Can you?

As Holmes and Watson climbed the steps of 221b Baker Street, they discovered a box sitting by the door. The lid of the box was square, and this square was divided into nine more squares. Inside each square (except one) was written a letter (see diagram below). Dr. Watson was about to open the box when he was abruptly stopped by Holmes. "I don't think that would be wise, Watson," said Holmes. "It doesn't look safe to me."

Can you identify the missing letter?

O	U	D
R		A
E	G	N

When Lady Sharp reported the kidnapping of her young son to Sherlock Holmes, Holmes knew that the crime could only have been carried out by one man—Professor Moriarty.

Lady Sharp produced a ransom note for £10,000. The note also carried a warning that should the money not be paid she would never see her son alive again. As Lady Sharp left 221b Baker Street, a note was delivered by hand to Sherlock Holmes. "Blast!" cried Holmes as he read the note before passing it to Doctor Watson. "Moriarty knows that we are on the case, Watson. We must act quickly if we are to save the life of Lady Sharp's son!"

Watson read the note. "I don't understand, Holmes. This note is nothing more than gobbledegook!"

"Not so, Watson," cried Holmes as he grabbed his coat. "Unless we find Moriarty's hiding place quickly, we will be too late to find Lady Sharp's son alive!"

The note read: HATED HALLS TEAK STREAM HARPS TOADY!

Can you decipher the note?

Sherlock Holmes sat opposite Inspector Lestrade in Lestrade's office at Scotland Yard. Sergeant Smith entered with three prisoners, who were stood in a line in front of Lestrade's desk. Holmes watched with interest as Lestrade interrogated the three men.

Barnett stood between the man who was clean-shaven and the man who had stolen a cigar case. Black, who had the stolen wallet, had been arrested at the same time as Wetherby. It was the man with the mustache, not the one with the beard, who had stolen the gold watch.

Can you identify each of the men, matching them to:
a) the item each had stolen.
b) whether each was clean-shaven, had a mustache or a beard?

Sherlock Holmes and Dr. Watson were enjoying a quiet game of dominos after dinner. At one stage during one of the games, they were each left with three dominos. With the exception of the double blank, they held all the doubles between them. If they were to add the spots on the three dominos they each held, Holmes's total would be two more than that held by Watson.

If Watson didn't have the double two and Holmes didn't have the double four, what were Watson's three dominos?

During the course of one night Professor Moriarty robbed five jewellers, taking only diamonds from each one. During his investigation, Sherlock Holmes discovered that one jeweller had lost 1/4 of the total diamonds stolen, another had lost 1/3, a third had lost 1/6, the fourth lost 1/12 and the last jeweller had lost a total of 22 diamonds.

How many diamonds had been stolen altogether?

Dr. Watson had spent the last hour trying to solve the remaining three clues in his daily crossword.

"Read them out, Watson," said Holmes.

"Each clue is a single word, Holmes. MAT, RAID and BLAZE," replied Watson.

Holmes thought for a moment. "Incidentally, Watson. I can make one word using the letters of those three words."

"That would be quite an act, Holmes," snapped Watson.

"Indeed it would, Watson. Indeed it would," replied Holmes.

Can you figure out the word Holmes was thinking of?

Sherlock Holmes and Dr. Watson spent some time talking to Mr. and Mrs. Small, who were the butler and the housekeeper at Fulton Hall. One of their children was suspected of stealing works of art from the hall and selling them to a local antique shop. During the conversation, it was established that Mr. and Mrs. Small had seven daughters. Each of the daughters had a brother.

Including Mr. and Mrs. Small, how many are there in the family?

Dr. Watson followed Professor Moriarty into a quiet avenue where there were only six houses, the numbers of which ran in sequence. He watched Moriarty enter a house before returning to Baker Street to report to Sherlock Holmes.

"What was the number of the house that Moriarty entered, Watson?" asked Holmes.

"I can't remember," replied Watson. "but I do remember that the sum of the six numbers was 666."

What was the highest of the six numbers?

Professor Moriarty had pulled off a large bank robbery and was in an overly generous frame of mind. He stood on a street corner and offered money to the first thousand adults who came by. He offered £10 to each man, and £20 to each woman. Of the men, only half accepted the money. Of the women, only one-fourth took the cash.

How much did Moriarty give away?

As Sherlock Holmes and Dr. Watson travelled by hansom cab to Scotland Yard, Holmes tested his companion with the following puzzle. Holmes handed Watson a piece of paper on which were written three groups of letters:

E C H.   T R W.   L ? O.

"Identify the missing letter," Holmes said.

Watson spent the whole of the journey trying to solve the problem without success.

Can you identify the missing letter?

In a year, Sherlock Holmes solved ninety more cases than Dr. Watson. Watson, in turn, solved seventy fewer cases than Inspector Lestrade. Sgt. White solved twenty more cases than Sgt. Black, while Lestrade solved forty more cases than Sgt. White.

If Watson and Sgt. White solved fifty cases between them, how many cases did all five solve in the year?

Mrs. Hudson, at the request of Inspector Lestrade, had baked a large number of loaves which were to be sold at a fund-raiser for retired police officers. At the fair, Mrs. Hudson sold the brown loaves for twice as much as the white loaves. But of the hundred loaves sold, only a quarter were brown.

If the brown loaves were sold at £1 for ten, how much did Mrs. Hudson raise for her efforts?

Sherlock Holmes and Dr. Watson were travelling by train from London to Edinburgh. Some distance into the journey Dr. Watson glanced out the carriage window. "There's a tunnel up ahead, Holmes," he announced. "According to the sign it is one mile long."

"That's interesting," replied Holmes. "We are travelling at 30 miles per hour and the train is 88 yards long. Tell me, Watson. From the moment the engine enters the tunnel, how long will it take before the last carriage emerges from the other end?"

Watson didn't have a clue. Can you find the answer?

As Holmes and Watson rode in a hansom cab from 221b Baker Street to Scotland Yard, Holmes gave Watson a note. On the note was written the following sequence of letters.

E O E R E X N ?

"Can you identify the next letter in the sequence?" asked Holmes.

"Give me a clue, Holmes," asked Watson, with a confused look on his face.

Holmes smiled, "If the letters were numbers, you'd probably find it much easier, old chap," he said.

Can you identify the next letter in the sequence?

Sherlock Holmes and Dr. Watson were following three criminals who had carried out a bank robbery to Euston railway station. Unfortunately, all three had managed to escape before Holmes and Watson arrived at the station. Holmes interviewed several railway employees and discovered that all three had boarded trains to different destinations. Parker, the leader of the trio, did not take the train to Carlisle. Davidson didn't take the Liverpool train and Costello didn't take the Glasgow train. He also discovered that the Carlisle train left the station before the train taken by Davidson. Holmes knew that each of the three had taken a train to one of the above-mentioned destinations.

Can you find out the destination of each of the criminals?

As five petty criminals left a tavern one evening, they were promptly arrested by Inspector Lestrade. After escorting them back to Scotland Yard, he made them take out the contents of their pockets. Between them they had some £70 in cash.

From the following information can you determine just exactly how much each of them had?

1) Brown had £3 more than Adams.
2) Clark had £3 more than Brown.
3) Drake had £6 more than Brown.
4) Evans had £12 more than Adams.

Dr. Watson was having a peaceful day fishing on the River Thames. He was having a very successful day because he caught eight fish in all.

From the strange phrase below (and using each letter once only), can you identify the three different types of fish caught by the good doctor?

PERTH CARROT CUP

Sherlock Holmes and Dr. Watson boarded a cruise liner during the pursuit of a killer. Information had led them to believe the man had bought a ticket to board the liner. The captain agreed to allow Holmes to interview all the passengers before the ship sailed. There were more than two passengers aboard the liner but less than one hundred.

If each passenger paid exactly the same amount in full pounds and the total amount collected in passenger fees came to £7,999, how many passengers were aboard the ship and how much did each of them pay?

While working on a series of robberies, Sherlock Holmes and Dr. Watson interviewed ten people, each of whom had a different occupation. Listed below are the ten occupations in anagram form.

Can you unravel each of them and identify the ten occupations?

1. STRIPE.　2. LEWDER.　3. LAMINAR.　4. REWARD.
5. CRANED.　6. HECTARE.　7. STINTED.　8. BREAK.
9. RESIGN.　10. CORKED.

Sherlock Holmes, Dr. Watson and Mrs. Hudson spent a relaxing evening playing poker for fun. Instead of money, they used playing chips. At the end of the evening, Mrs. Hudson was left with half as many chips as Watson, while Holmes was left with three times as many chips as Mrs. Hudson.

If the total amount of chips was 750, how many chips did each of the three have at the end of the evening?

Sherlock Holmes and Dr. Watson had followed two counterfeiters to their secret printing place. They waited outside for quite some time before bursting in and taking the two men by surprise. Next to the printing press they found some £5,000 in forged bills. Holmes then asked the two men to empty out their pockets. Thereupon Holmes recovered £227 more in forged bills.

If one forger had £55 more than the other, how much did each of them have in his pocket?

Mrs. Hudson was returning from the fruit and vegetable market when she bumped into Dr. Watson.

"I hope you remembered to buy some onions," said Watson.

"If I had $1\frac{1}{2}$ more onions, then I would have $1\frac{1}{2}$ times as many," replied Mrs. Hudson.

Dr. Watson scratched his head in confusion.

Can you deduce how many onions Mrs. Hudson had in her basket?

Sherlock Holmes and Dr. Watson were called to the Royal Mint, where they were informed by an executive that there was at least one thief in the building. Over a period of several days, a large number of gold coins had disappeared. Holmes decided to set a trap. He placed a box containing a number of gold coins in an area where it was easily accessible to everybody in the building. He and Watson then hid themselves behind some large cabinets to observe the scene. After a few minutes, a man appeared, looked inside the box and removed a third of the coins. Only seconds later, the man returned and removed a third of what remained. Some 10 minutes later, another man appeared and he proceeded to remove a third of what remained. Holmes then checked the box to find that only eight gold coins remained.

How many gold coins had originally been in the box?

Sherlock Holmes and Dr. Watson were retracing the movements of Professor Moriarty after a recent robbery. Their inquiries had taken them to a little industrial-supplies shop in Ealing. The owner of the shop recalled that Professor Moriarty had been a customer several days ago. The shop owner had sold Moriarty a chain saw for £16 plus half as much as he had originally paid for it.

If the shop owner's profit was £7, how much had he originally paid for the chain saw?

Professor Moriarty was about to carry out a daring robbery with two other criminals, Stoneface Murphy and Fingers Malloy. In order that none of them would be recognized, they each wore a false beard. They were also armed. One carried a rifle, another a pistol and the third a club. Moriarty entered the bank behind the one who wore the false brown beard and in front of the one who carried the club. Fingers had used the pistol in a previous robbery and was disappointed that he didn't have it on this occasion. It was the one with the false red beard who carried the club.

If Fingers did not wear the false brown beard, who carried the club?

Sherlock Holmes had solved the remaining four answers to Dr. Watson's crossword puzzle. The four answers were: FALL, HILL, CAST and POUR. "Tell me, Watson," said Holmes, as he passed the newspaper back to his colleague. "Which same four-letter word can be added to the front of each of those answers to give four more good English words?"

Can you think of the four-letter word?

Sherlock Holmes had been hired to find three boys who had run away from home. His inquiries had taken him to the London docks and, in particular, the ocean liner *Celestial Star*. After carrying out a search of the ship, the three boys were discovered hiding inside one of the ship's lifeboats.

"How old are they?" exclaimed the captain as the boys stepped onto the deck.

"Their combined age is 27 years," replied Holmes. "Tommy is twice as old as Eric, while James is three-quarters the age of Tommy."

Can you deduce the age of each of the three boys?

Sherlock Holmes and Dr. Watson were in the small kitchen of Fredrick Blake, the retired gardener at Greenacres Mansion. Fredrick lay dead on the floor, the victim of a ghastly murder.

Dr. Watson pointed to a stain on the wooden floor-boards where Fredrick lay. "This looks like some sort of acid burn, Holmes," he said.

"Very observant of you, Watson," replied Holmes. "Take a look at these items on the kitchen table. There are acids contained in each one of them. Can you name them, Watson?"

The items on the table were: 1. Vinegar.   2. Green apples. 3. Tea.

Can you name the types of acid in each case?

In a warehouse, Sherlock Holmes came across some crates set out in a triangle (see diagram). All the crates (apart from the one at the head of the triangle) were numbered.

Can you deduce the number of the last crate?

A friend of Sherlock Holmes invited him to spend the weekend at his country cottage. On the first morning, Sherlock Holmes enjoyed several duck eggs for breakfast. "Those eggs were really tasty," said Holmes to his friend. "Do your ducks lay eggs often?"

"Let's put it this way," replied his friend. "A duck and a half lays an egg and a half in a day and a half."

How many eggs will 6 ducks lay in 7 days?

During a cricket match, Sherlock Holmes scored ninety more runs than Inspector Lestrade. He, in turn, scored seventy less runs than Inspector Brown. Dr. Watson scored twenty more runs than Sgt. Smith. Inspector Brown scored forty more runs than Dr. Watson.

If Inspector Lestrade and Dr. Watson scored fifty runs between them, how many runs did all the above players score altogether?

Dr. Watson entered 221b Baker Street just as the housekeeper, Mrs. Hudson, stepped on the scales to weigh herself.

"Be careful not to break those scales, Mrs. Hudson," he said with a smile.

"Are you trying to insinuate that I'm overweight?" she snapped.

"Of course not," said Watson, somewhat tongue in cheek. "But out of curiosity, just how heavy are you?" he asked.

"I'm exactly 79 lbs. plus half my own weight," she replied.

What was Mrs. Hudson's correct weight?

Sherlock Holmes spent some two hours browsing through an antique shop before finally deciding to make several purchases. He spent half the money that he had in his wallet on a silver figurine, then half of the money he had spent on the figurine on a brass candlestick. Holmes was then left with £6.25.

How much money did Holmes spend on the figurine?

Sherlock Holmes and Dr. Watson were about to interview three men regarding a recent robbery at Fanshaw Manor. The three men were sitting outside Inspector Lestrade's office in Scotland Yard.

"Who are they?" asked Watson.

"A Mr. Black, Mr. Grey and Mr. Brown," replied Holmes.

"How amazing," said Watson, "They're wearing suits that match their names."

"Perfectly correct, Watson," said Holmes, "But not one of them is wearing the precise color of suit that matches his own name."

"Then Mr. Black is wearing the brown suit," said Watson with some confidence.

"Not so," replied Holmes.

Can you deduce the color suit each of the three men was wearing?

Sherlock Holmes studied the dead victim who lay on the library floor. Dr. Watson entered the room. "I've spoken with the maid and she is quite adamant that she heard the shot ring out at 12:15 pm, Holmes," he announced, "which completely destroys your theory that the deed had taken place some time earlier."

"I still feel she is mistaken, Watson," said Holmes with some confidence.

"I doubt it, Holmes," replied Watson. "She was dusting in the study when she heard the shot. She remembers standing bolt upright at the sound of the blast and she remembers looking directly into the mirror and seeing the clock behind her. It was unmistakably 12:15 pm."

Holmes smiled at his colleague, "Then I was correct all along, Watson," he exclaimed.

What time did the maid actually hear the shot?

Professor Moriarty swindled five businessmen out of a total of £1000. From the first he swindled £20 less than he did from the second. From the second he swindled £20 less than he did from the third. From the third he swindled £20 less than from the fourth, and from the fourth £20 less than he did from the fifth.

How much did he swindle from each of the men?

While sitting in his study, Sherlock Holmes was handed a piece of paper by his colleague, Dr. Watson. On the paper was written the following sequence of numbers:

45	32	31	42
34			37
38			41
33	44	43	30

"What is this, Watson?" asked Holmes.

"This is my magic square," Watson replied. "The numbers add up to the same total in each direction. But I have deliberately left out the four center numbers. Can you tell me what they are?"

Watson was disappointed that Holmes was able to supply the numbers within a matter of seconds.

Can you do it?

Professor Moriarty had set up a system of robbing all the houses on an exclusive London street. The street contained twenty-five houses and they were numbered accordingly.

On the diagram below, can you fill in the question marks with the correct number of houses to complete the system?

?	24	1	8	15
23	?	7	14	16
4	6	?	20	22
10	12	19	?	3
11	18	25	2	?

Sherlock Holmes, Dr. Watson, Inspector Lestrade and Sgt. Smith were all playing for the Scotland Yard select cricket team in a charity match. While in the locker room getting ready for the match, each of the four accidentally put on the jersey belonging to one of the others.

From the following information can you figure out whose jersey each of them was wearing?

1. Watson wasn't wearing the jersey that belonged to Lestrade.
2. Holmes didn't wear Watson's jersey nor vice versa.
3. Sgt. Smith went to bat ahead of the person wearing Watson's jersey.

Sherlock Holmes and Dr. Watson were walking along a quiet street when they both observed the following sequence of letters written on a wall:

I C A B
I C A U
I C A X
I C A P

Below the sequence of letters was written: One of these rows of letters does not belong to the series. Which one?

Holmes was quick to supply the answer. Can you?

While working on a murder case, Sherlock Holmes, Dr. Watson and Inspector Lestrade found themselves searching a desolate Yorkshire moor for the murder weapon. During the search, they were assisted by a police sergeant and a constable. Before the weapon was found, every one of them had covered a lot of ground in their search.

From the following information, can you deduce just exactly how much ground was covered by Inspector Lestrade?

1. Holmes, Watson and the constable had covered 9 miles between them.
2. Lestrade, Watson and the sergeant covered 16 miles.
3. Watson, Holmes and Lestrade covered 12 miles, while the total number of miles covered by Lestrade and the constable was 7.

Sherlock Holmes, Dr. Watson, Mrs. Hudson, Inspector Lestrade and Sgt. Black all decided to spend a night in a supposedly haunted mansion. Just before midnight, they all travelled (in separate hansom cabs) to the country mansion.

From the following information, can you figure out which one of them arrived fourth at the mansion?

1. Watson's cab arrived before that of Black, but behind the cab carrying Lestrade.
2. Mrs. Hudson's cab arrived before Watson's, but behind the cab carrying Holmes.

Sherlock Holmes and Dr. Watson were called to a jewelry shop on Oxford Street where a number of precious stones had been stolen in a daring robbery.

From the following information, can you deduce just how many diamonds were stolen?

1. The combined total of diamonds, rubies and garnets stolen was twenty-nine.
2. The combined total of rubies, garnets and sapphires stolen was thirty-one.
3. The combined total of diamonds and sapphires stolen was eighteen.

Dr. Watson was sitting in the study of 221b Baker Street examining the night sky with his telescope when Sherlock Holmes entered the room and passed him a piece of paper.

"Written on the paper, Watson, is a series of letters," said Holmes. "Since you are observing the stars, you should have little difficulty finding the three missing letters from the series."

On the paper was written the following sequence of letters:

S U I R A ? ? ?

Can you complete the series?

Professor Moriarty and three of his criminal colleagues rushed from a hardware shop, each carrying a handful of money which they had stolen from the poor owner. In total they had £94. Moriarty had £13 more than Bloggs, who in turn had £5 less than Norris, while Hunt had £3 more than Moriarty.

Can you deduce how much each of the four carried individually?

Sherlock Holmes had been called to a small London hotel to investigate a series of robberies from rooms occupied by guests.

Can you place each guest in the exact room he occupied in the hotel from the following information (see diagram below)?

(12 bedrooms)

3rd floor				
2nd floor				
1st floor				

1. Messrs. Smith, Idle and Law were all on the floor above the floor where Messrs. Jones and Grey had their rooms.
2. Mr. Black's room was directly above the room occupied by Mr. Davis and directly to the right of the room occupied by Mr. Grey.
3. Messrs. Green, Adams and White were all on the floor below the floor where Mr. Wilson had his room.
4. Mr. Brown's room was directly above that of Mr. Jones, who in turn was directly to the right of Mr. Wilson.
5. Mr. Idle had Mr. Law directly to his right.
6. Mr. White was directly below Mr. Grey and directly to the right of Mr. Adams.

While spending a weekend fishing in the country, Sherlock Holmes and Dr. Watson were asked to investigate a series of robberies that had taken place at three cottages which were situated close to the fishing lodge where they were staying.

From the following information, can you name the family that lived at each cottage and the item they had had stolen by the robbers?

1. The Madisons didn't live at No. 3, nor did they lose a gold watch.
2. The O'Connors didn't live at No. 5.
3. £50 was stolen from No. 3.
4. The Newtons didn't live at No. 1, where a crystal decanter was stolen.

Five pickpockets were arrested by Inspector Lestrade on evidence supplied by Sherlock Holmes. They were escorted back to Scotland Yard, where they were found to have some £95 in cash between them.

From the following information, can you determine just exactly how much each of them had?

1) Smith had £3 more than Jones.
2) Montgomery had £4 more than Smith.
3) Marr had £5 more than Jones.
4) Morgan had £12 less than Montgomery.

While serving a prison sentence in Wormwood Scrubs prison, Professor Moriarty made five separate escape attempts on each day from Monday to Friday. On each attempt, he tried a different method: a) Disguised as a prison officer. b) Tried to tunnel from his cell. c) Attempted to bribe a prison officer. d) Exchanged identity with a visitor. e) Attempted to sneak out with a work party.

From the following information, can you determine which method was used on which day?

1. Moriarty attempted to escape disguised as a prison officer two days before his attempted bribe of a prison officer.
2. He tried to tunnel out of his cell the day after his attempt disguised as a prison officer.
3. His attempt to sneak out with the work party didn't take place on Monday or Friday.
4. Moriarty exchanged identity with a visitor the day after his attempt to join the work party.

Sherlock Holmes, Dr. Watson and Inspector Lestrade travelled to different parts of the country following up the trail of a gang of criminals. In all, they covered 294 miles between them.

If Watson covered twenty more miles than Lestrade and Holmes covered twenty more miles than Watson, how many miles did each of them cover?

Dr. Watson purchased six garden ornaments, which he duly placed around the back garden at 221b Baker Street, only to find that when he awoke the next morning some thief had made off with them all. "They cost me a fortune," he complained to Sherlock Holmes. The six items had individually cost Watson £4, £10, £12, £15, £18 and £24.

From the following information, can you work out the exact items for each of the above prices?

1. The statue of Peter Pan cost £3 less than the statue of Admiral Nelson.
2. The fishing gnome cost £8 more than the hanging basket.
3. The reading gnome cost £14 less than the small fountain.

As a result of excellent work by Sherlock Holmes, the infamous Professor Moriarty was being held in the special security wing of Wormwood Scrubs prison. In all, there were twelve cells in the special wing, four on each landing (see diagram below).

From the following information, can you place each prisoner in his proper cell?

1. Little's cell was on the landing directly below the landing where Robb and Gunn had their cells.
2. Pearce's cell was directly above Conn's cell, who was on the landing above the landing where Hobbs and Webb had their cells.
3. Field had his cell directly to the right of Webb's cell and was directly below the cell occupied by Robb.
4. Tibbs had his cell directly to the left of Milne's cell, who was directly above Moriarty.
5. Kidd's cell was directly to the left of the cell occupied by Pearce.
6. Moriarty was in the cell directly above the cell occupied by Webb.
7. Hobbs's cell was directly below Gunn's cell.

The infamous Professor Moriarty had masterminded a massive bank robbery which meant a loss of many thousands of pounds for the bank concerned. By the time Sherlock Holmes had been called in to investigate the robbery, it had been discovered that five leather pouches containing valuable Spanish gold coins had also been stolen. The gold coins totalled 111 in all.

From the following information can you figure out how many gold coins were contained in each of the five pouches?

1. The combined number of coins in pouches 1 and 2 was 40.
2. The combined number of coins in pouches 2 and 3 was 35.
3. The combined number of coins in pouches 3 and 4 was 42.
4. The combined number of coins in pouches 4 and 5 was 54.

Answers

Puzzles of Deduction • Answers

1 1 The numbers represent the vowels, 2 = A, 3 = E, etc. Then by breaking the message up into words, it reads: Tomorrow I will steal the crown jewels. This will be my greatest triumph.

2 13 The wine in the smaller glass was one-sixth of the total liquid, while the wine in the larger glass was two-ninths of the total. Add these together to reveal that the wine was seven-eighteenths. Therefore the poison content had to be eleven-eighteenths.

3 25 Holmes was travelling to Manchester, Watson to Edinburgh and Lestrade to Brighton.

4 37 Craig had £92. Albert had £85. Bobby had £50.

5 49 Father and mother were 36 yrs. old. The three children were triplets, all aged 6 yrs.

6 61 John committed 7 offenses, Harold 12 offenses and Robert 18.

7 73 116

8 85 Holmes 375. Watson 250. Mrs. Hudson 125.

9 97 158 lbs.

10 108 8 diamonds

11 2 Fish 22 yrs. Hill 33 yrs. Giles 66 yrs.

12 14

7	4	8	=19
2	9	5	=16
6	3	1	=10
=15	=16	=14	⟍ 17

13 26 Wilson. The code numbers were devised by taking each letter of the member's surname and relating each one to its place in the alphabet. A = 1, B = 2,

etc. Wilson consists of the 23rd, 9th, 12th, 19th, 15th and 14th. Added together they make 92.

14 38 The guests arrived as follows: 7:30 Lord Winterbottom. 7:45 Sir Harry Trump. 7:50 Lady Barclay. 7:59 Sir John Penn. 8:05 Lady James. 8:20 Lord Hadden.

15 50 Fred

16 62 5 boys and 6 girls

17 74 £5000

18 86 One forger had £141 and the other had £86.

19 98 £12.50

20 109 U, Q and A. The complete series reads: S U I R A U Q A, Aquarius spelled backwards.

21 3 £48

22 15 22 + 2 = 24

23 27 William Ewart Gladstone (the Prime Minister)

24 39 Lestrade called at 22 taverns, Watson 19 and Holmes 16.

25 51 R. All the others are the initial letters of the numbers one to ten.

26 63 Lefty had the most money. Shifty had the least.

27 75 J. The first letter of each group is followed by the letters that come two before and three after it in the alphabet.

28 87 3 onions

29 99 Mr. Brown (black suit), Mr. Black (grey suit), Mr. Grey (brown suit)

30 110 Moriarty had £28, Bloggs £15, Norris £20, Hunt £31.

31 4 12 points. 5 pts. were awarded for first place, 2 pts. for second and 1 pt. for third.

32 16 N (for ninety)

Puzzles of Deduction ● Answers

Ans. Puz.

33 **28** 1. 12 pairs of brothers
2. 18 pairs of uncles and nephews

34 **40** Mr. Baker/Andrews Street.
Mr. Andrews/Dawson Street.
Mr. Clark/Easton Street.
Mr. Dawson/Baker Street.
Mr. Easton/Clark Street.

35 **52** From left to right: Ace of
Diamonds, Ace of Hearts, King of
Spades, Queen of Diamonds, Ten of
Clubs, Queen of Hearts

36 **64** Pile one = 1,250. Pile two
= 750. Pile three = 350.

37 **76** 250 cases

38 **88** 27 coins

39 **100** 11:45 am

40 **111** The bedrooms were occupied as follows:

Smith	Brown	Idle	Law
Wilson	Jones	Grey	Black
Green	Adams	White	Davis

41 **5** No. 5 Aston Avenue

42 **17** The letter "e"

43 **29** Arthur is the bald-headed
doctor. Bert is the banker with brown
hair. Clive is the grey-haired accountant.

44 **41** Holmes 42 points, Watson
28 and Lestrade 14.

45 **53** Mrs. Hudson ate 24 pies.
Watson 16, Lestrade 10 and Holmes 8.

46 **65** Sparkling, Sparking, Spar-
ing, Spring, Sprig, Prig, Pig, Pi and finally "I."

47 **77** £6.25

48 **89** £18

49 **101** £160, £180, £200, £220
and £240

50 **112** The Madisons lived at
No. 1 and lost the decanter. The Newtons
lived at No. 5 and lost the gold watch.
The O'Connors lived at No. 3 and lost
the £50.

51 **6** A coffin

52 **18** West

53 **30** 38 diamonds

54 **42** 15

55 **54** Bookkeeper

56 **66** S. Going around the square
from the top righthand corner spells out
the word "dangerous."

57 **78** 2 minutes and 6 seconds

58 **90** Fingers carried the club.

59 **102**

45	32	31	42
34	39	40	37
38	35	36	41
33	44	43	30

60 **113** Montgomery had £24.
Marr had £22. Smith had £20. Jones had
£17. Morgan had £12.

61 **7** Andrew Richards, Frank
Andrews, Richard Franks

62 **19** 3 years old

63 **31** M. The sequence repre-
sents the letters on the bottom row of a
typewriter as they run from left to right.

64 **43** Come quickly, Holmes.
There's strange goings on at Baskerville
Hall.

65 **55** Hopkins is the vice-
chairman. White is the chairman. Smythe
is the secretary. Knight is the treasurer.

66 **67** Death shall take Master
Sharp today.

125

Puzzles of Deduction • Answers

Ans. Puz.

67   **79**   T. Each letter is the last letter of a sequence of numbers: on(e), tw(o), thre(e), etc. The last letter is that of the number eigh(t).

68   **91**   Down. Downfall, Downhill, Downcast and Downpour.

69   **103**   Each column adds up to 65.

17	24	1	8	15
23	5	7	14	16
4	6	13	20	22
10	12	19	21	3
11	18	25	2	9

70   **114**   Monday: Disguised as a prison officer.
Tuesday: Tried to tunnel from his cell.
Wednesday: Tried to bribe a prison officer.
Thursday: Tried to join the work party.
Friday: Exchanged identity with a visitor.

71   **8**   No. 24. The pattern: $4 \times 4 = 16 - 4 = 12 \div 4 = 3 + 4 = 7 \times 4 = 28 - 4 = 24$

72   **20**   6 ft 4 in

73   **32**   52 ($-10, +9, -8, +7, -6, +5, -4 = 52$)

74   **44**   28 guests

75   **56**   Here is one possibility.

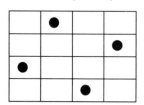

76   **68**   Barnett: Mustache. Gold watch. Wetherby: Beard. Cigar case. Black: Clean-shaven. Wallet.

77   **80**   Parker was aboard the Liverpool train, Davidson aboard the Glasgow train and Costello aboard the train bound for Carlisle.

78   **92**   Tommy 12 yrs. James 9 yrs. and Eric 6 yrs.

79   **104**   Holmes was wearing Lestrade's jersey, Watson was wearing Smith's, Lestrade wore Watson's and Smith wore Holmes's.

80   **115**   Holmes 118 miles. Watson 98 miles. Lestrade 78 miles.

81   **9**   Lestrade was wearing the overcoat belonging to Holmes, while Holmes wore Watson's and Watson wore Lestrade's.

82   **21**   Lestrade wrote 42 pages, Holmes wrote 37 pages and Watson 20 pages.

83   **33**   Lestrade rode Tinkerbell, while Martin rode Spring Goddess.

84   **45**   27 cakes

85   **57**   95

86   **69**   Double four (8), double five (10) and double one (2). Total: 20.

87   **81**   Adams had £8. Brown had £11. Clark had £14. Drake had £17. Evans had £20.

88   **93**   1. Acetic acid. 2. Malic acid. 3. Tannic acid.

89   **105**   I C A X. The other letters when read aloud all mean something: I see a bee, I see a ewe, I see a pea.

90   **116**   Hanging basket £4, reading gnome £10, fishing gnome £12, Peter Pan £15, Admiral Nelson £18, small fountain £24.

91   **10**   Deadline, cathedral, forebear, hobgoblin and science

92   **22**   Mrs. Hudson, Holmes, Watson, Sgt. Black and Lestrade

93   **34**   300 times

94   **46**   4 years ago

95   **58**   18 pockets

Puzzles of Deduction • Answers

Ans. Puz.

96 **70** 132 diamonds

97 **82** Perch, carp and trout

98 **94** The number of the last crate is 38. The number on each crate is found by adding together the number of the two crates directly above it.

99 **106** 5 miles

100 **117**

Tibbs	Milne	Kidd	Pearce
Gunn	Moriarty	Robb	Conn
Hobbs	Webb	Field	Little

101 **11** The boy is Watson's nephew and his sister's son.

102 **23** 41 and 28 (69), 46 and 33 (79), 21 and 8 (29)

103 **35** 54 lbs.

104 **47** They would stand the signpost up so that the arm indicating the village they had just come from was pointing in the right direction. The other arms would then automatically point correctly too.

105 **59** 3/1

106 **71** Dramatizable

107 **83** The liner had 19 passengers, each paying £421.

108 **95** 28 eggs

109 **107** Watson

110 **118** Pouch 1 = 22 coins. Pouch 2 = 18. Pouch 3 = 17. Pouch 4 = 25. Pouch 5 = 29.

111 **12** Giggling

112 **24** 27 days

113 **36** Inspector Lestrade occupied seat number 39, while Sergeant Baxter had seat number 37.

114 **48** Mary

115 **60** The gardener is the butler's great-grandson.

116 **72** 10. Mr. and Mrs. Small, their 7 daughters and their 1 son.

117 **84** 1. Priest. 2. Welder. 3. Railman. 4. Warder. 5. Dancer. 6. Teacher. 7. Dentist. 8. Baker. 9. Singer. 10. Docker.

118 **96** 250 runs. Sherlock Holmes 100 runs. Inspector Lestrade 10 runs. Inspector Brown 80 runs. Sergeant Smith 20 runs. Dr. Watson 40 runs.

Index